the BOX that
CHRISTMAS
came in

OTHER PRODUCTS BY DEBBIE HARMAN:

My Baptism Day: The Best Day Ever

Cooking for Two

The Book of Mormon Says . . .

The Creative Companion CD-ROM series

the BOX that CHRISTMAS came in

Debbie Harman

Covenant Communications, Inc.

Cover image: *A Wonderful Gift* by Li Kim Goh © iStockphoto

Cover design copyrighted 2007 by Covenant Communications, Inc.

Published by Covenant Communications, Inc.
American Fork, Utah

Printed in Canada
First Printing: October 2007

14 13 12 11 10 09 08 07   10 9 8 7 6 5 4 3 2 1

ISBN 13: 978-1-59811-459-1
ISBN 10: 1-59811-459-X

DECEMBER 1984

It had been a particularly harsh winter in the sleepy hamlet of Sanpete County, Utah. Denny Harman pulled the woolen cap down over his ears as protection against the frosty air, then tugged at his gloves and picked up the snow shovel. The sun was just starting to dance along the edge of the horizon, and a new set of dark gray storm clouds was rolling into the valley from the east. He knew that within an hour it would be snowing in earnest—and he wanted to make sure the walks were cleared from the previous night's storm before the new one pounded the valley.

Normally, Denny would have been out in the early hours of the morning shoveling his walks—as well as those of Erma Olson, a sweet widowed neighbor who had become like a second mother to him and Ann. But he and Ann had spent the day in busy preparation for a trip north, and there had been no time to attend to the walks. Pausing at the edge of the porch, Denny cast a worried look at the western sky. It was likely to be a treacherous trip with that kind of storm on the horizon, but they had no choice . . . They *had* to go.

As he wiped his brow with the sleeve of his heavy coat, Denny had to chuckle. He suddenly remembered all the years in Arizona. As a young man, he had started working in the copper mine. The money had been good enough to provide well for his growing family. And the winters certainly hadn't been like this! He laughed a little as he used the edge of the snow shovel to chip away at the ice that had collected at the bottom step. The few times it had snowed in Arizona each winter, the clouds had surrendered nothing more than a skiff of snow, and even that had melted in the bright sunlight before the miners all stopped for lunch. Denny laughed again as he realized he had never even owned a snow shovel until he moved to Manti.

It had been a heart-rending decision for Denny and Ann to leave their life in Ajo, a pleasant little town only forty miles from the Mexican border. They had been well-liked in the community, and the members of the Church had been their family—the way members *should* be, like real brothers and sisters. It had been their home, but they went on nothing but faith and determination to the farming community of Manti, Utah. It had been a tough choice, but as their oldest daughter graduated from high school and they considered her future, they realized they needed a new environment for their children, who were rapidly approaching marriage age. So they had bid farewell to their friends, the mine, and their financial security, settling in a hundred-year-old home just a few blocks from Temple Hill.

Those had been lean years, Denny recalled. He grabbed up construction jobs, welding jobs, and any other work he could to make ends meet for the family. Ann tried to be happy as she learned to cook on the old wood-fueled cook stove, which was also one of their main sources of heat. She made at least three quilts for every bed from the coat scraps left behind at the nearby sewing factory where she worked part-time. When spring finally came, Ann carved out a good-sized garden plot and taught her children to plant and care for the produce. They rejoiced at their first harvest, feasting on a single potato that was large enough to feed the entire family. They raised chickens and pigs and learned to get by on whatever the Lord saw fit to provide. Yes, those had been lean years, Denny remembered—but, oh, how he had grown to love Ann through those years of sacrifice. She had given up so much, and together they had worked tirelessly to make sure their children thrived in that little valley shadowed by the beautiful temple.

As he finished shoveling Erma's walk, the first flakes of snow started drifting lazily through the air. Denny stopped and did what he had seen his own children do a thousand times: opening his mouth as wide as he could, he tipped his head back, stuck out his tongue, and caught the first few snowflakes of the late afternoon. Smiling, he shuffled through the snow toward the old shed to put away his shovel.

* * *

Looking up from the sink full of hot, sudsy water, Ann saw Denny—nose and cheeks rosy from the bitter cold—carrying a large apple box toward the house. She smiled as she realized that she had rarely seen this man without something in his arms. He had always been busy helping someone in need, and was always the first on the scene when anyone needed help. The sound of Denny kicking snow off the toes of his boots punctuated the late afternoon stillness of the house, and he burst through the back door and dropped the box on the table. "We need to get going, Ann. The snow won't hold off for long," he said, draping his large arm across her small shoulders. "I'm worried about getting through Nephi Canyon."

Ann wiped her hands on the dishtowel and stacked the last of the dishes in the cupboard. She could never leave until every dish was done and her house was in order. "Do you think we should stay home?" she questioned.

"No!" Denny responded quickly. "We are going. We are on a mission! The Lord will have to take care of us, because we *have* to go!"

That was that. Once Denny had his mind set, there was no changing it. He pulled a large frozen turkey from the freezer and called out, "Ann, get the lid!"

Ann hurried to the table and pulled the lid from the apple box. After he placed the turkey in the box, Ann said, "Denny, I can take care of this. You go get the car ready." Denny was no stranger to helping in the kitchen. He liked cooking and helping whenever he could. But Ann liked to do things in a more gentle, organized way—and because Denny loved her soft touch, he obeyed when she hinted that she could take care of things . . . her way.

Ann patted the turkey resolutely. "They're going to love you!" she said. She then lifted the brown paper grocery sacks onto the table next to the box and started tucking food around the solidly frozen bird. There were cans of cranberry sauce, a small sack of potatoes, a bunch of celery, cans of soup, and even some oranges and apples. She managed to fit a small bag of flour at one end and cartons of eggnog and butter tucked in at the corners. She covered the top with ingredients for fudge and some small boxes of Jell-O and pudding.

Just as she finished, Denny came in the door with a sense of urgency. "Just about finished up?" he asked. "It's starting to snow hard. We need to get on the road right away!"

"It's all packed up," Ann replied. "Can you please take it to the car while I get my coat?"

Denny strained to lift the heavy box and managed to get it loaded into the trunk. As they both settled into the front seat, he bowed his head in prayer and asked for the Lord's protection as they made their way through the storm to their destination. Eager to make their way north, Denny eased the car onto the already-slick road and headed out of town. "I sure wish we'd been able to get those new snow tires on Monday," he mumbled. "I'd feel a lot better driving these roads with a little tread under me!"

The sun had set, and the headlights cast an eerie glow through the swirling snow. As they traveled further north of Manti, they were the only people on the road. The storm increased in intensity until it became a blizzard. Denny tensed behind the wheel and thought again of his balding tires. What a difference that new set of snow tires would have made! There was nothing he could do about it now, though, and he uttered a silent prayer as he slowed the car and tried to stay in his lane.

He and Ann talked with anticipation about the upcoming holiday, the gifts they still needed to buy, and the expected arrival of their daughter and her family. He tried to keep the conversation light, but Denny's hands gripped the steering wheel tightly and his heart beat rapidly with fear. The roads were getting worse, and visibility was nearly zero. He couldn't remember ever driving this route through such a bad storm.

Ann finally turned to him, placing her hand on his arm. "Do you think we should turn back?" she asked quietly.

"No!" he replied. "We *have* to get there. What will they do if we don't?"

"You're right. Can we stop for just a minute and offer another prayer?"

Denny eased onto the shoulder of the road and turned off the engine. Together they offered a heartfelt prayer for safety in reaching their destination. Explaining to Heavenly Father the urgency of delivering the box, they trusted the success of the trip to His care, then resumed the drive.

As they crept into Utah County, they were crestfallen to discover that the storm was even more intense there. Denny found himself a hundred yards behind a snowplow that was attempting to clear the far right lane. It was an obvious blessing from above, and he slowed to match the plow's careful speed. They would arrive later than planned . . . Hopefully things would still work out.

The street lights lining the freeway illuminated the falling snow, and the scene was one of great beauty. Denny drove slowly and carefully the last sixty-five miles of their journey, and finally eased off the freeway in West Valley City just before ten. They drove along the familiar streets, parking just around the corner from the modest two-story apartment building.

"You stay here," Denny said with a smile to Ann. "The box is too heavy for you to carry, and I'm not sure at all that you could make a quick getaway on the icy steps."

Ann laughed. "I think you're right," she replied. "Be careful!"

Denny wrestled the heavy box out of the trunk and walked carefully down the snow-packed steps to the basement apartment. What if they weren't home? Worse yet, what if they were just getting home and caught him in the act? What if the curtains were open, and they saw him? What if they had all gone to bed?

He shook his head to clear his thoughts. It was all going to be fine. Leaning against the cold cement wall, he caught his breath. Just a few more yards, and he'd be home free.

The little mat in front of the door was covered with snow. He tried to brush it aside as best he could with his boot. He stooped down, placed the box on the mat, stood again, and paused to catch his breath. What looked like the glow from a single lamp was visible through the thin living room curtains. Inching as far away from the door as he could, he leaned on the doorbell and then ran for the stairs.

He was safely out of sight when he heard the door open. There was silence. The snow fell steadily, and the night air was cold and crisp. Finally he heard it—a man's voice edged with astonishment. He couldn't quite make out what the voice was saying, but he knew the mission had been completed.

Denny slipped from behind a large pile of snow at the corner of the building, a remnant of the plows that had cleared the parking lot. He heard a woman's voice carried on the air. Denny was filled with such happiness, it seemed he floated back to the car. Once inside, he leaned across the seat and kissed Ann. "They got it!" he cried. "We made it!"

Tears welled up in Ann's eyes. "Oh, Denny, I think this just might be the best part of Christmas for me this year," she replied, leaning her head on his shoulder. With joy in their hearts, they started the 120-mile journey back to Manti through what would later be hailed as the worst storm of the year.

* * *

It was a week before Christmas, and they had absolutely no money. None. They were struggling to meet the expenses of their six-week-old twin girls, who had recently been released from the newborn intensive care unit. They had paid what they could on the staggering medical bills. To make matters worse, there was no food in the apartment.

Rick had considered asking for an advance on his paycheck; since payday was only three days away, he figured his boss would be willing to help him out. But as they discussed it, they decided that wasn't a good idea—the money from that paycheck was already designated for rent, utilities, and other expenses.

They snuggled together on the couch, reviewing their other options. Each held a sleeping twin, sweet and perfect in her innocence. The hour was late, and they were becoming desperate.

"What about going to your parents' house?" Sheri asked. "Could you get a couple of days off? They'd love to see the girls, and we could spend a few days with them. Your mom would be happy to prepare some of her famous Christmas meals!"

Rick weighed the prospect carefully before he answered. "Deb, I just think it's too dangerous right now," he said. "The streets are already snow-packed, and the storm is supposed to last for a couple of days. If it were just us, maybe I'd consider it—but I just can't put the girls at that kind of risk."

Sheri nodded. "Yeah, you're right," she responded. "I guess it really would be foolish to try to make a trip in this kind of weather." As much as she tried to fight off the discouragement, the tears started flowing. She wiped her cheeks with the sleeve of her nightgown.

Rick gathered her against him with his free arm. "Deb, it's going to be okay," he assured her. "I don't know how, but we're going to be okay. Besides," he added quietly, gazing down at his new daughter, "we got the best Christmas gift of all. We have Marci and Megan, and they're home and healthy. That sort of puts everything else into perspective, doesn't it?"

Sheri smiled as she nodded and surveyed the sweet infant in her own arms. That blessing truly did eclipse the fact that they had no money and no food.

Suddenly the doorbell rang.

"Who on earth could that be at this time of night?" Sheri asked.

"And in this outrageous storm?" Rick added. "Anyone with any sense should be barricaded in their nice, warm apartment!" He handed Marci to Deb and made his way to the door. A blast of icy air pounded him as he opened the door.

No one was there. Just as he was about to shut the door, he glanced down. There, squarely situated on the welcome mat, was an apple box overflowing with food. "Deb, come here," he said, his voice edged with astonishment. "You're not going to believe this."

Sheri struggled to get up with an infant in each arm. She nestled the girls on the sofa and went to the door. Her mouth dropped open, and the tears again ran down her cheeks.

"What on earth?" she asked. Rick stooped down, picked up the heavy box, and took it to the kitchen. Sheri followed, flipping on the kitchen light. She lowered herself onto a chair, tucking her feet beneath her for warmth.

"Rick, who on earth could have done this?" she asked as he started pulling one item after another out of the box. The bounty covered the kitchen table.

"I don't know," he said quietly, "but whoever it was, it's an answer to prayer." He grabbed Sheri and pulled her into a tight embrace. The two wept with joy, then looked again at each item from the box.

NOVEMBER 2002

"You girls had better get up!" Grandpa called down the hallway. "Spencer and your dad will be back with the tree soon!"

Groggy from too little sleep and sprawled with her two sisters on their grandparents' living room floor, Megan opened her eyes. It wasn't even light outside. She closed her eyes again and imagined her father and brother somewhere in town, poking through the evergreens in a Christmas tree lot.

This had become one of her favorite traditions—visiting her grandparents in Provo and helping Grandma and Grandpa get ready for Christmas. It had been a tradition ever since Grandpa and Grandma had been forced to move from their old pioneer home in Manti to Provo, where Grandma could be close to a hospital. They had moved into a beautiful brick home just a few blocks from their oldest daughter, Denan.

The entire family was thrilled that Grandma finally had a new home with so many modern conveniences— including a dishwasher and *three* bathrooms. And it was counted as a great blessing when Grandpa, who had been working with the Church's facilities management group, was allowed to transfer to Utah County. Everyone was so happy for Grandpa and Grandma, but Megan couldn't lie—she was heartbroken. As long as she could remember, her grandparents had lived just a few blocks away from her house in Manti.

Megan and her twin, Marci, were barely six months old when they'd moved to Manti—and their grandparents' home had been their second home. She missed Sunday dinners, with everyone gathered around the big dining room table. She missed stopping on the way home with her brother and sister, when Grandma always invited them in for a cookie break. Thinking about it now, she could almost taste the warm cinnamon sweetness of Grandma's snickerdoodles!

She missed walking past the old tabernacle on Main Street and having Grandpa greet her and all her friends with a big smile and a hug. He had always been like a big kid to them. On St. Patrick's Day, he painted his hair green to avoid any mischievous pinches. And every Halloween, he dressed up in a different costume.

But six years ago, Grandpa and Grandma had left Manti and moved to Provo. Though it was a necessary move, it had been a challenge for Megan and her family. Used to daily interaction with these much-loved people, they now lived just far enough away that they didn't get to visit often. And so they especially loved spending this time at Thanksgiving with their grandparents each year.

The girls loved stringing lights around the big window in the living room. They always used great care to take each piece of the Christmas village out of its box and to painstakingly set it up. They always worked meticulously to arrange the porcelain Nativity set. Grandma had lost most of her speech, but she loved to watch from her wheelchair as the girls transformed the house. She often giggled when a certain decoration emerged from its box or laughed with delight when a certain piece of the Christmas village was put in place.

But this year it just wasn't the same. Usually, the girls

would sleep in while their parents went Christmas shopping and while Grandpa and Spencer picked out a Christmas tree. While they were all gone, the girls would help Grandma decorate the house. There was always plenty of time, since Grandpa insisted on inspecting every single tree at his favorite lot two or three times in order to find the perfect one. By the time they arrived back home with the tree, the girls were finished with the house and ready to decorate the tree.

That was how it usually worked. This year, however, things were different. Grandpa was slowly recovering from cancer treatments, and was too weak to shop for a tree; everyone was alarmed to see how frail he had become as a result of the chemotherapy. Just months earlier his strong, broad frame had towered over everyone else; now that very frame was thin and bent, resting heavily on a wooden cane.

Even though he looked different on the outside, he was still the same playful Grandpa on the inside. He was already up and ready to go, with gallon jugs of fresh-squeezed apple juice lined up on the kitchen counter for the girls who came to bathe Grandma and fix her hair.

He had been doing Grandma's makeup and hair for years. In fact, he had been doing *everything* for her . . . and had been cooking, cleaning, washing and folding the laundry, and maintaining the yard as well. But that was before the cancer.

Denan tried to help, but Grandpa was proud, and resisted relying on his daughter. Then his son, Lenny, moved in with his family for a few months during the worst of the chemotherapy treatments. But when it seemed that Grandpa was on the mend, they'd moved back home.

Grandpa tried to resume everything he'd been doing, but it simply wasn't possible. He had surrendered his strength to the powerful cancer treatments, and was heart-broken to find that he could no longer even care for his sweet wife. That's when the caregivers arrived on the scene. Grandpa treated them like his own granddaughters. As they bathed his wife and did her hair and makeup, he sat nearby and chattered with them about school and boys, dispensing his advice with a smile. And today, he had a little Thanksgiving gift to show his appreciation: fresh-squeezed apple juice, golden amber in the gallon jugs.

Megan listened for a minute to her grandfather's good-natured talking in the kitchen. *We'd better get up,* she thought to herself, *or Grandpa's going to embarrass us.* At that, she sat up and kicked off the quilt that lay over her on the living room floor. She shook first Holli, then Marci.

"Get up, you guys," she said. "Grandpa is ready to start decorating—and you know what that means." The girls laughed quietly. Grandpa was like the captain of a ship, always trying to keep things moving. He had a way of putting everyone to work, making sure that no one escaped without a job. Even this year, exhausted and weak, he was trying to get everyone organized and moving between his trips to the kitchen to chat with the caregivers.

Somehow, Grandpa's orders never seemed to bother the girls. In fact, it was wonderful to see him acting more like his "old self" again. The girls hauled in boxes of Christmas decorations from the garage and began stringing lights around the big picture window. Megan removed the burned-out bulbs, and Holli replaced them with new ones. Marci plugged the sets together and made sure everything was working.

As they moved on to the other decorations, Grandpa reminisced, telling stories about each one; Grandma sat in her chair and smiled at the memories. Grandpa had always told great stories, but this year he seemed more sentimental than ever.

This year, Grandpa started out by telling the girls they were all princesses. "There are plenty of fish in the sea," he counseled them, "so if you find one that doesn't treat you like a princess, toss him back!" As the girls laughed, Grandpa added, "In fact, toss him up on the beach so that *nobody* has to have him!" Grandma laughed knowingly and tried to nod her head as Grandpa looked each girl squarely in the eye until each one promised him she would never settle for a boy that treated her as less than the princess she was.

While they were arranging the Nativity set, it suddenly occurred to Megan that her grandparents might not be around much longer, and the thought washed over her with drenching sadness. As they worked to arrange the finely detailed porcelain pieces, Grandpa quietly bore his testimony of the Savior; at its conclusion, he looked upward with tears in his eyes. "We're going home soon, aren't we?" he said to Grandma. Megan felt the hot tears burn her eyes. Her grandparents were elderly, and this was inevitable, but she wasn't ready to lose them . . . not yet.

The stillness of the moment was shattered as Rick and Spencer bolted through the door with the Christmas tree. "Okay!" Grandpa enthused, "let's start decorating the tree!"

* * *

By the time Sheri arrived home from Christmas shopping, the family was almost finished trimming the fragrant evergreen.

The minute she walked in the door, she could feel that something was different. The Spirit was so strong . . . she couldn't *see* anything different in the room, with its familiar collection of festive decorations, but she had never felt such an atmosphere of peace within the walls of that home. Both she and Rick sensed deeply that Grandpa and Grandma wanted them to linger, so they canceled plans to visit friends in Salt Lake and stayed another day in Provo.

It was just past eleven that night when Sheri, overcome with exhaustion, excused herself and went to bed. Over the next few minutes, the girls and Spencer settled down for the night, too. As she drifted off to sleep, Sheri could hear the muffled sounds of her husband and her father-in-law talking at the kitchen table.

A few hours later, Rick snuggled in beside Sheri. "I'm sorry I'm so late coming to bed," he whispered. "It seemed like my dad wanted to talk all night. I feel bad, but I just couldn't keep my eyes open any longer."

He drew Sheri closer to him and said, "I have to tell you a story."

Sheri, who had been drifting in the fog somewhere between sleep and awareness, sensed the serious urgency in her husband's voice and forced herself to become alert. "Okay," she said. "What's up?"

There, in the quiet darkness of the guest room, warm beneath the patchwork quilt, Rick related the story of his parents—Denny and Ann—and the treacherous trip they had made eighteen years earlier to deliver an apple box filled with all the fixings for a wonderful Christmas feast. It had been a miracle for the young couple who had received it—and now, eighteen years later, they'd finally realized that the angels who carried it to their small basement apartment were their own parents.

The tears ran down Sheri's cheek, soaking the warm pillow. "I had no idea it was them," she finally said. "Why didn't they ever tell us?"

"I don't know," Rick replied. As they lay together in silence, Rick drifted off to sleep, but Sheri watched a small shaft of moonlight on the ceiling and thought about that night eighteen years earlier. These wonderful people had blessed them so, and they had not even suspected who it was. As she thought about all the traditions that had started as a result of that snowy night eighteen years earlier, Sheri, too, surrendered to sleep.

Eager to get on the road the next morning, Sheri was waiting for the perfect moment to thank her in-laws—but with all the chaos involved in getting a busy family back on the road, the opportunity slipped by. Several times that weekend, Sheri vowed that she would call to thank Grandpa and Grandma for the tremendous example they were, but something else always came up to distract her. Then, on Sunday night, the terrible news arrived.

Grandpa was in the hospital. He had suffered a series of seizures, and it looked like the cancer had invaded his brain. He needed immediate radiation treatments—and the prognosis was poor.

The news spread fast, and everyone shared the same reaction. How could this vital man—this strong, capable leader of the family—be slipping away so quickly? Arrangements were made for Sabrina, Robert, and their family to come from Alaska for Christmas; Sandi, Stan, and their family agreed to come from Las Vegas. And, of course, Rick and Sheri and their children would go to Provo from Manti.

* * *

It was a tradition to celebrate Christmas at the home of Uncle Charles and Aunt Denan. And keeping with the tradition from their Arizona roots, they always enjoyed a Mexican dinner on Christmas Eve that featured tamales, enchiladas, and other entrees from south of the border. That year the house was filled with even more laughter, because everyone in the extended family had arrived to celebrate Christmas. Each came through the door with an armload of beautifully wrapped gifts and dressed in festive attire. Memories were shared and little ones excitedly shared what they wanted Santa to bring that night as the family raved over the delicious tamales.

After dinner, everyone gathered in the family room for the traditional Christmas Eve program. Grandpa was too tired to read the story, so he passed the Bible to Uncle Charles. As Charles began reverently reading from Luke the story of the Christ child's birth, each of the younger grandchildren carefully placed a piece of the hand-carved Nativity set in the center of the living room carpet. One by one, the shepherds appeared, watching over their sheep. Then the wise men, with camels, approached from the east. Soon cattle and donkeys joined the scene. Chubby little hands placed first Joseph, then Mary in the center of it all. Finally, the littlest child held his breath as he carefully positioned the manger and then lovingly placed the baby Jesus inside.

There were a few minutes of silence as the family gazed on the Nativity, eyes moist, thinking about the birth and life of the Savior. Then Sheri's heart began to pound, and a lump formed in her throat. As she gazed at the Nativity and thought of the Savior's great sacrifice for all of them, she began to remember the great sacrifices of their parents.

She glanced at Denny and Ann, and then looked

around the room at all their posterity. How their sacrifice in leaving Ajo had proved fruitful! This family was what really mattered to them, and—sick as they both were—she could see the joy shining in their eyes.

As was the tradition, Uncle Charles stood to read a special Christmas story—this new one he'd found since the last time they had gathered on Christmas Eve. Everyone, even the littlest children, listened quietly to the words . . . everyone, that is, except Sheri. All she could hear was Grandpa's voice and Grandpa's story, a story of love and sacrifice. She looked again toward Grandpa and Grandma. He sat slightly slumped over with pain but trying to hide his discomfort; his arm was resting by Grandma's wheelchair as he tenderly held her hand. It was clear to Sheri that he was trying to enjoy every last minute with the family he loved so much.

Uncle Charles finally finished, and there was silence for a few seconds. Then excitement erupted as the group, true to tradition, began to sing Christmas songs. *Why didn't I say something?* Sheri asked herself. *I should have shared the story. Everyone in this family should know what our parents did for us.* . . .

Finally the group burst into the strains of the last song, "Cactus Christmas Tree." The familiar words rang through Sheri's head as she sang along. As the last verse ambled toward its finish, Sheri felt her jaw begin to tighten and her hands begin to tremble. As soon as the song ended, Sheri abruptly stood in the corner of the room where she'd been sitting.

"Wait," she said. "I have a Christmas story, too, and I want to share it with all of you who are here."

Several of the faces around the room registered surprise. All eyes were on Sheri as she made her way to the front of the room, where Charles had been standing. Nobody said a word.

"My story is a true story, and it happened eighteen years ago," Sheri began. "Rick and I had just moved into an apartment complex in West Valley City. We didn't know very many people because our little twins, Megan and Marci, were just six weeks old. Some of you remember that they had been in the newborn ICU for a while. It was an especially harsh winter, and we didn't dare take our babies out very much when it was so cold. So we pretty much kept to ourselves.

"It was a very scary time for us. Although Rick had a job, it was a temporary job, and our future looked pretty bleak. His pay was not good, and we had a mountain of hospital bills. Just a week before Christmas, we had finally reached a point where we didn't have any money at all, and we didn't have any food in our house."

Everyone sat quietly, focused on Sheri. Even the littlest children were eagerly waiting to hear what happened next.

"We were desperate," Sheri continued. "We didn't know what to do. We felt so alone. We talked about several possibilities, but none of them were feasible. We were sitting on the couch, trying to figure out a solution, when the doorbell rang. It was late at night, and there was a terrible snowstorm. We couldn't figure out who would be out at a time like that.

"Rick finally answered the door, and there on the step was a large cardboard apple box," she said. Eyes grew wide as little children imagined the scene. "He looked around but couldn't see anyone. He brought the heavy box in the apartment, and inside was a large turkey, and food stuffed in every possible corner. The food lasted us for a week.

"We started guessing who had done this for us. Our first

thought was the youth in the ward; it was just the kind of service project they would do for the holidays. Then we decided it might be our upstairs neighbors. I quickly put together a small Christmas gift and took it upstairs. The young mother acted so appreciative! That night, she and her husband brought down a Christmas gift for us. We visited for a while, and it was the beginning of a rewarding friendship. But it was obvious they had not brought us the box.

"We decided it had to be one of our other neighbors, so we made simple gifts for each of them. Our gesture created a rippling effect, and soon we received gifts from each of them in return. With each delivery, we began to know our neighbors a little better, and friendships started to grow. We also noticed that everyone was exchanging gifts with everyone else in our complex. We were amazed at the profound effect of one small act and were thrilled to watch the spirit of Christmas spread throughout our entire building.

"Rick and I vowed that we would remember that experience, and that we would share what we had with others every Christmas," Sheri said. "Many of you know about our Christmas box tradition, but some of you don't. Every year, our whole family chooses someone we would like to secretly give to. We all work together to create a wonderful Christmas box that will meet that family's needs. Then we deliver it anonymously one week before Christmas, just as our Christmas box was delivered to us. I think it's the best part of our Christmas season.

"The first year we chose a single mother, because we knew that she needed the assurance that someone cared about her. We remembered hearing her comment once that when you are single, the holidays can be very difficult. We filled a box with food, and Rick delivered it the week before Christmas; it meant so much to her.

"The next year we decided on a young couple who was struggling financially. We filled a box with holiday food, as usual, but this time Rick took some money from our Christmas fund, tucked it in an envelope, and secured it carefully in the box. Because we would not be able to provide as nice a Christmas for our own children, we explained to them what we had done. To our surprise, they were excited.

"Every year the anticipation grew about who would receive our Christmas box. One night as we were discussing it, Marci quietly suggested we should give the box to Ruth, as it was her first Christmas in sixty years without her husband.' We all agreed—Ruth would get the box. But since part of our gift to Ruth was recognizing her loneliness, we delivered her box in person, so we could all visit with her."

Rick and Spencer nodded their heads in agreement; Megan began to softly cry at the memories of their Christmas boxes. Suddenly there were other sniffles. Sheri looked up and saw that both of Rick's parents were crying. The tears dripped from Grandpa's cheeks onto the sleeve of his shirt, and Grandma's shoulders trembled with her silent weeping.

"I just found out a few weeks ago who brought us that first Christmas box," Sheri said, struggling to control her own emotion. "It was Grandpa and Grandma. Grandma lovingly stuffed that apple box with as much food as she could, and then they drove more than 120 miles each way in a terrible storm to drop it at our door. They never said a word about it. They let us believe all those years that it was someone else—and now I hope they know that their act of such great love has been multiplied many times over. It is their example and their love that created in our family the desire to share whatever we have with others. Theirs is the greatest example I could ever ask for."

As Sheri crossed the room and embraced Rick's parents, no one else moved. Suddenly it dawned on her! Standing beside them, she spoke quietly. "Now I understand why you finally told Rick that you delivered the box," she said. "You wanted to make sure we never forgot—that we would never let the tradition die. Oh, we won't! That's our promise to you!"

There was not a dry eye in the room. Grandpa and Grandma smiled at each other through their tears; Sheri wiped away her own tears, straightened her shoulders, and tried to speak loudly enough through her emotion to be heard.

"Normally, we deliver our Christmas box anonymously the week before Christmas. This year, we're breaking with tradition. Mom, Dad, we decided last September that *you* were going to receive our Christmas box this year. It was going to be a secret. We were going to leave it on the doorstep and run. But I think it's okay if we do it this way."

Sheri nodded at Rick, who grabbed Spencer and went out to the car to retrieve the Christmas box from the trunk. Once back inside, they set it ceremoniously at the feet of Grandpa and Grandma. Everyone in the room watched with excitement as Grandpa pulled one item after another from the box, exclaiming with joy at each one and lovingly draping the lap quilt across Grandma's frail frame. As Sheri watched through her tears, she saw not her parents-in-law at a family gathering, but a young couple in a modest apartment building in West Valley City, exclaiming with joy over the answer to a prayer. And the others in the room saw not only a Christmas box but a loving couple who had sacrificed throughout their lives and who demonstrated the real meaning of Christmas.

The Christmas box had come full circle.

EPILOGUE

That was the last Christmas Eve Rick and Sheri had with Grandma and Grandpa. Grandpa died in February, a victim of the cancer he had fought so bravely. Grandma followed him in June. She had spent more than a dozen years confined to a wheelchair, showing by example the meaning of patience and endurance. Her attitude was not one of complaint, but one of simple gratitude for the blessing of being able to remain with her sweetheart and her family. Together they set a marvelous example for their entire family.

Sheri couldn't help but think of *Where the Red Fern Grows,* of big Dan and little Ann. But in her story, it was big Denny and little Ann. One couldn't live without the other, and now they are together forever, never to be separated again.

Every time Sheri walks into a grocery store produce section and sees the stack of apple boxes, she is reminded of their wonderful father—a father who was willing to drive hundreds of miles in a severe snowstorm to bring them a Christmas surprise. He was close enough to the Spirit to know what they needed. And he didn't care about the sacrifices it required. He simply wanted to make sure his children had food to eat when they were hungry.

And she thinks, too, of the effect his gift has had over almost two decades. That first Christmas box inspired her family to share whatever they had. Perhaps it inspired the recipients of their boxes to do the same. Over the years, they have been remarkably blessed by knowing the true meaning of Christmas as they have sacrificed and shared, just as her father-in-law did.

As she ponders the story of her father-in-law and that first Christmas box, she can't help but think of another Father. That Father so loved the world that He sacrificed His Only Begotten Son for all of us . . . and she knows He smiles each time one of us emulates the Savior of all mankind.

Rick's father wanted them to know before he died that he'd brought the gift because he wanted them to always remember how much he loved them. Our Father in Heaven, too, wants us to remember Him and to know how much He loves us. As part of that, He has asked us to remember His Son, which is a special privilege each Christmas season.

As we rejoice in the miracle of Christmas, we feel the love of our Savior. If we are willing to share that love with others—not only at Christmas, but throughout the year—there will be a wonderful ripple effect that will spread through our families, our wards, our neighborhoods, our places of employment. Wounds will be healed. Broken hearts will be mended. There will be peace and joy and the hope that comes from the knowledge of our Savior.

I pray that all of us might share what we have with others, and that we might especially share the love of the Savior, so that all of us might feel as Rick and Sheri did on that night so many years ago. We are not alone. We are loved. Our needs will be met. We are part of a family whose Eldest Brother has paved the way for all of us to go home again . . . home in the true Spirit of Christmas.

ABOUT THE AUTHOR

Debbie Harman studied art at Snow College, where she met and married her husband, Ken. Since then, Debbie has created several best-selling clip-art products for Covenant and has illustrated a number of children's books.

Debbie and Ken have four children and live in Manti, Utah, in a 112-year-old house that they renovated. Debbie has served in the Relief Society and Primary programs, and is currently serving as stake Young Women's president.